S0-BIU-036

Contents

In This Issue

Features

The Lost City of the INCAS

Article by Rebecca Green

Machu Picchu—
Facts and Figures

Location: about 112 km north of Cuzco, Peru
Altitude: 2430 m above sea level
Surrounding: semi-tropical jungle
Built: 15th century C.E.

Have you heard stories about the lost city of Atlantis—buried under the sea after a huge earthquake? Fact or fiction? Nobody knows. Atlantis has never been found, so we'll probably never know whether it actually existed. It's hard to believe that a whole city could go undiscovered for hundreds of years, but in the case of Machu Picchu *(mah-choo-pee-choo)*, that's exactly what *did* happen.

High in the Andes mountains of Peru live the descendants of the Incas—an ancient civilization that once stretched from Colombia to the centre of Chile and had a population of more than 12 million. For years, people have been interested in this mysterious civilization. They had no written language with which to pass on their stories, but they left behind some of the most incredible **architecture** in the world.

When the Spanish invaded Peru in the sixteenth century, they tried to destroy the Incan culture and convert the people to their own way of life and religion. They destroyed the Incan structures and took the gold and silver the Incas had used to decorate their buildings. They **looted** the temples and built churches in their place.

However, the Incan people continued to live among the ancient walls built by their ancestors, and still do to this day.

The Rise and Fall of the Incan Empire

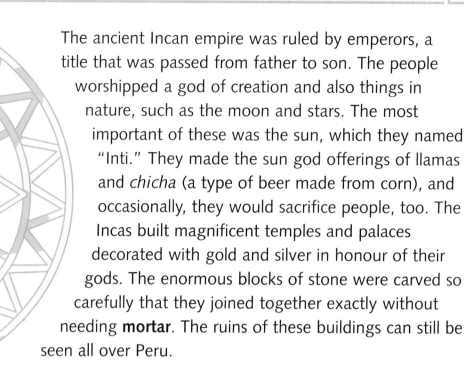

The ancient Incan empire was ruled by emperors, a title that was passed from father to son. The people worshipped a god of creation and also things in nature, such as the moon and stars. The most important of these was the sun, which they named "Inti." They made the sun god offerings of llamas and *chicha* (a type of beer made from corn), and occasionally, they would sacrifice people, too. The Incas built magnificent temples and palaces decorated with gold and silver in honour of their gods. The enormous blocks of stone were carved so carefully that they joined together exactly without needing **mortar**. The ruins of these buildings can still be seen all over Peru.

Unfortunately, the gold and silver that was so common in Peru was also highly valued by the Spanish explorers. In 1532, an explorer named Francisco Pizarro captured the Incan emperor, named Atahualpa *(at-a-wal-pa)*, and demanded a room full of gold and a room full of silver as ransom. The ransom was paid, but Pizarro killed Atahualpa in 1533. The Spanish invaders continued to **persecute** the Incan people, and the last emperor, Tupac Amaru, was killed by them in 1572. Although this was really the end of the empire, the **indigenous** people of Peru survived, and the **descendants** of the ancient Incas continue to live high up in the Andes.

Cuzco was the capital of the Incan Empire. Many of the ancient stone walls and temple still stand today.

The Search for the Lost City

In 1911, an explorer and professor from Yale University named Hiram Bingham set out from the city of Cuzco along the Urubamba River. He travelled on foot and by mule through the Peruvian jungle in search of an ancient Incan city. He believed this was the long-lost capital of the Incas.

It might seem incredible to think that a whole city could be "lost," but in 1911, much of the Peruvian jungle was still **uncharted** territory. Hiram Bingham chose a route that followed the course of the river. It was not an easy journey—at one point he had to cross a dangerous bridge over some rapids. The bridge was made from a few logs tied together with vines. He crawled across slowly on his hands and knees, wondering what would happen if the river should rise any further. Just beyond the bridge, he met some local farmers. They had been in the area for four years and told him about some ruins nearby. Bingham set off with a young boy who acted as his guide.

Hiram Bingham

QUADOR

COLUMBIA

PERU

BRAZIL

Machu Picchu

Cuzco

BOLIVIA

CHILE

ARGENTINA

THE INCAN EMPIRE

MACHU PICCHU

AGUAS CALIENTES

Urubamba River

OLLANTAYTAMBO

URUBAMBA

POROY

CUZCO

Machu Picchu

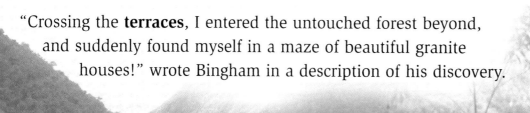

"Crossing the **terraces**, I entered the untouched forest beyond, and suddenly found myself in a maze of beautiful granite houses!" wrote Bingham in a description of his discovery.

When he pushed back the jungle and saw perfectly constructed Incan walls, Bingham knew that he had discovered something very important. At first, he couldn't see how large the ruin was because it had been buried in the jungle for so long. In many places, houses were completely covered by plants, and huge tree trunks sprouted from the ancient walls.

Most of the buildings in the city were made from granite blocks cut with bronze or stone tools.

Bingham had discovered an ancient city of the Incas, which had been left untouched for many hundreds of years. Today we know it as "Machu Picchu," which means "Old Peak" in the language of the local people. We will never know what the original name of this settlement was because it had been abandoned for so long. After the discovery of Machu Picchu, Bingham continued travelling through Peru, but returned to Machu Picchu in 1912 and 1915 to **excavate** the site.

The architects and engineers that built the city were experts. The blocks of stone had been measured so accurately that Bingham couldn't even slide a ruler between them.

It seems the Spanish never found Machu Picchu. How could they have missed it? It's quite simple—the ancient city is surrounded by high cliffs, which keep it hidden from view and make it very difficult to reach. Perhaps the Incan people had already left the city when the Spanish arrived, and it was long forgotten. With no maps to follow and no one to guide them, it's not surprising the Spanish missed it.

We will never know why the city was abandoned because there's no one left to tell us. Maybe the people left after a battle with another tribe, or the population could have been wiped out by an epidemic.

Today, **historians** think that Machu Picchu was built for important royal and religious members of Incan society, possibly to protect them from attack. The size and design of the buildings show that the most important people would have been living in its palaces.

A thousand people could have lived in Machu Picchu, and they would have been completely **self-sufficient**. They had enough food, water, and shelter for everyday life.

The Inca Trail

Today, Machu Picchu is considered one of the most important **archaeological sites** in the world, and every year more than 300 000 people travel to Peru to visit it. There are two ways to get to Machu Picchu. You can either take the train from a nearby village or you can follow the ancient route that the Incas would have taken—trekking through the jungle and over high mountain passes for four days.

Following the trail, you can imagine what it must have been like for Hiram Bingham and the Incas before him. As you reach the end of the trail and climb the final staircase to "the sun gate," the whole of Machu Picchu appears below you—a lost city in the depths of the jungle.

Machu Picchu

Machu Picchu is a complete city with temples, houses, palaces, storage buildings, and **bathhouses**. None of the buildings have roofs now because they would have been **thatched**. The site is divided into three sectors— agricultural, urban, and religious.

Agricultural Area

In the agricultural area, terraces are cut into the hillsides. These made it possible to plant crops on steep slopes and also prevented erosion. The stone walls prevented the soil from being washed away. The Incas planted crops such as corn and potatoes in the terraces.

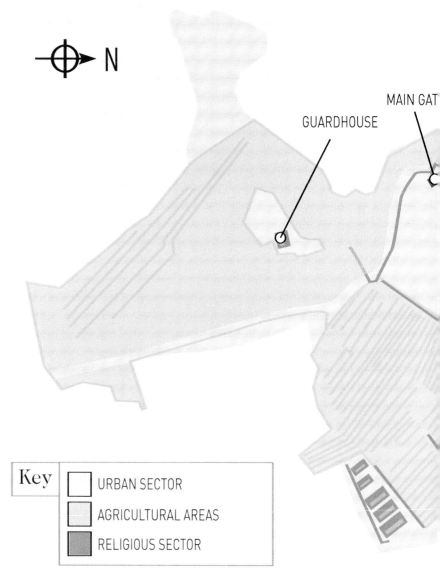

N

GUARDHOUSE

MAIN GAT

Key
URBAN SECTOR
AGRICULTURAL AREAS
RELIGIOUS SECTOR

The religious sector has the most magnificent examples of Incan stonework, including a circular tower called the Temple of the Sun. The priests would have lived in this sector.

One of the most interesting constructions is the "Intihuatana" (*in-ti-wa-ta-na*) or "Hitching Post of the Sun." The Incas worshipped the sun and built these stone columns so that twice a year, on the winter and summer **equinoxes**, the sun would shine directly onto the post, creating no shadow at all. The Incas would hold special ceremonies to prevent the sun from abandoning them by "tying" it to the earth.

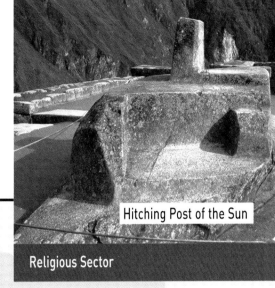
Hitching Post of the Sun

Religious Sector

TEMPLE OF THE SUN

HITCHING POST OF THE SUN

?RY

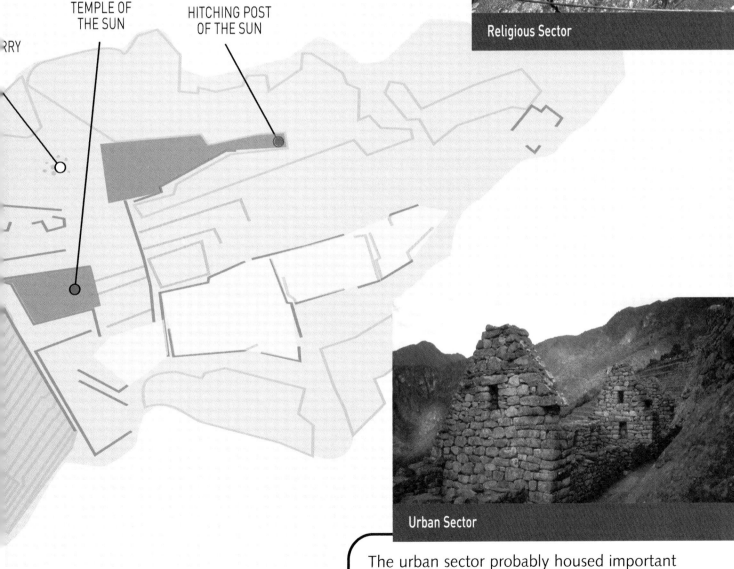

Urban Sector

The urban sector probably housed important teachers, the **intellectuals** in Incan society. There are also fountains, a jail, and an open area that separates this area from the religious sector.

SKIMMING AND SCANNING

Look at the article on finding lost treasure—"X Marks the Spot!"

- Flip through the pages, looking at the illustrations and diagrams, and read the first sentence of each paragraph.
- Now find the part in the text that tells you why so many people have dug and drilled on Oak Island.

SKIMMING AND SCANNING

You've just used two techniques called skimming and scanning.
We skim a text when we want to get a general idea of what the writing is about. There are several ways of doing this. You can

CAPTAIN KIDD'S TREASURE, OA

- read the first few paragraphs, a few in the middle, and a few at the end

- read the first and last sentences of each paragraph

- glance at the pictures, diagrams, charts, and captions to help you understand the main ideas in the text

We scan when we need to look for one particular detail and don't need to read the entire text. To be able to scan well you need to

- use headings, diagrams, and boxed and highlighted items to help you

- work out how information is organized (by sections, paragraphs, bulleted lists, or charts)

- look for keywords and phrases

TRY IT OUT

Look at the article, "Lost Memories."

- Skim the text, reading the first and last sentences of each paragraph, to get the general idea of what the article is about. When you have finished, write a few sentences to summarize what you have understood.

- Scan the text to find out what can cause amnesia. Write a few sentences to show your understanding.

- When you've finished reading the article in detail, look back at your notes. Did skimming the text beforehand give you the main idea of what the article was about?

FOR REAL

Research assignments often require you to work through information from different sources. You could search the Internet or even scan through a DVD, as well as read printed materials. The techniques of skimming and scanning can speed up your search for **relevant** information and help you to complete your assignment.

X Marks the Spot!

Article by Jane Buxton

Beneath the ground in many parts of the world lie secret **hoards** of ancient treasure, buried long ago and still waiting to be discovered. While most of us think it's the stuff of fairy tales, some people take the hunt for buried treasure very seriously.

Mysterious Oak Island

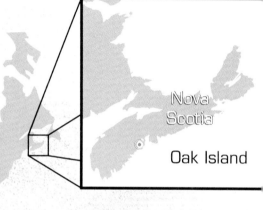

Nova Scotia

Oak Island

On Oak Island in Nova Scotia, treasure hunters have been digging and drilling for more than 200 years. But so far, nothing valuable has been found!

The story of Oak Island begins in 1795, when teenager Daniel McGinnis came upon a mysterious circular hollow in the ground. Hoping to find pirate treasure, he returned with two friends and began to dig.

The three young men continued their search for years, encouraged by small, **tantalizing** finds. Every 3 metres, they found layers of oak logs, and at 27.5 metres, they uncovered a large stone with a message in strange symbols. Later, some people thought they'd cracked the code and that the message said "40 feet below this stone, 2 million pounds are buried." So they continued to dig, but unfortunately, at a depth of about 30 metres, seawater flooded into the "money pit," and they were forced to abandon it.

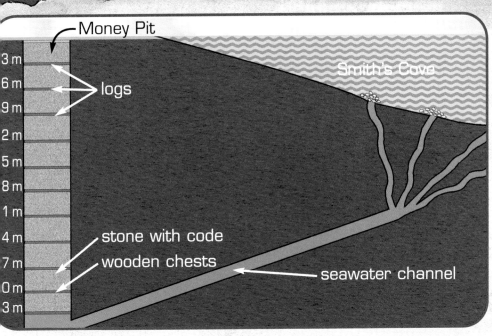

Money Pit

3 m
6 m
9 m
2 m
5 m
8 m
1 m
4 m
7 m
0 m
3 m

logs

Smith's Cove

stone with code
wooden chests
seawater channel

In 1849, the next hopeful seekers drilled at the Oak Island site. Reports say that the drill went through layers of oak wood and pieces of loose metal. The treasure hunters were sure they'd discovered oak chests filled with coins. Excited, they began to excavate, but flooding forced them to give up. It looked like a series of channels from a nearby beach caused water to flood into the pit when anyone tried to reach the treasure. Whoever first dug the pit had designed a very effective booby trap.

Over the years, picks and shovels and horses have been replaced with cranes and bulldozers, and recently new **geotechnologies** have been used to help with the search. What keeps people looking for treasure at Oak Island?

Some say Captain William Kidd, one of the most famous pirates of all time, buried his treasure there. Another theory is that the French stashed money on Oak Island for safekeeping during their battles with the English.

Most people say there's no evidence for any of these ideas. Items found in the pit, such as the engraved stone, have all mysteriously disappeared. Perhaps they, like the treasure, only ever existed in the minds of the hopeful seekers. We'll probably never know.

SEEKING CAPTAIN KIDD'S TREASURE, OAK ISLA

The Mildenhall Treasure

Some of the world's most famous finds have been completely unexpected. In Great Britain in 1943, a farmer named Gordon Butcher unearthed a large metal dish from a field near Mildenhall. He told his employer, Sydney Ford, who was a keen collector of antiques. The two men dug farther and, to their astonishment, they uncovered a huge assortment of ancient eating **utensils**. They were all black with age and apparently made from **pewter** or lead.

Ford displayed the collection on his **mantel** for three years until someone realized its value and reported it to the authorities. The treasure is now held by the British Museum and has been valued at around $120 000.

The Great Dish

A large bowl

A large water bowl for washing hands at the dinner table

A plate for serving food

So how could this old collection of spoons and plates be worth so much money? It was because the items were not made from pewter or lead, but from silver. There are thirty-four pieces in all, making it the largest hoard of Roman silver ever found in Britain.

The treasure was probably buried in the fourth century C.E., a time when Romans controlled Britain. No one really knows where the silver came from, but some experts think it may have belonged to a soldier from the Roman army who was later ordered back to Italy. He may have buried his silver for safekeeping but never managed to return to reclaim it.

Mystery surrounds the origins and history of the Mildenhall collection. As in most tales of long-lost treasure, memories become blurred and the stories change with the passing of time. We'll never know who the treasure really belonged to and why they never returned to claim it.

A statue of a Roman soldier

EATING SNOW

Story by Feana Tu'akoi

Illustrations by Ian Lien

Boof! Shen hit the snow again. He hauled himself up on one elbow and glared down the slope at his stepfather. "Marc!" he hollered. "Wait up!"

Marc turned expertly on his skis and headed back up the slope.

"Eating snow again, eh, Shen?" he joked. He reached out a hand to pull him up.

Shen ignored him. He shrugged off his backpack and got awkwardly to his feet.

Marc smiled. "Hey, it's no big deal," he said. "You're just tired. Maybe you shouldn't push yourself so hard."

Shen shook the snow off his clothes and checked his skis. "I can handle it," he snapped. He heaved the bag back onto his shoulders. "It's this thing that's the problem—it weighs a ton. We don't need all this stuff for one day."

Marc shrugged. "I hope you're right," he said. "But backcountry skiing can be dangerous. You have to be prepared for everything."

Shen shook his head as he picked up his ski poles, but he didn't say anything.

"All set?" asked Marc. "We'll get going, then. Only a couple more hours to go."

A couple more hours? Shen nearly groaned out loud. There had to be a quicker way. "Hey," he said, pointing at a long slope to their right. "Let's go that way—it's much more direct. It'll save us half an hour."

Marc looked in the direction Shen was pointing and rubbed his chin. "I don't know," he said eventually. "It looks all right, but it faces north, which could mean avalanches. I'd rather be safe and go out the way we came in."

"Oh, come on!" snapped Shen. He peered over the ridge and down the slope. "If we go this way, we'll have the wind behind us and a clear run to the bottom."

Marc studied the area carefully. "I guess it's okay," he said. "The slope's about twenty degrees—it's safe, as long as it doesn't get any steeper."

"It's fine," said Shen. "Let's go!"

"One at a time, then," Marc said firmly. "Just in case."

Marc zipped up all his clothing, loosened his pack, and took the straps off his poles. Then he watched while Shen did the same. "If we do get caught, we don't want to get weighed down," he said. "And make sure your radio's on transmit and turned to maximum. That way we can find each other if something goes wrong."

Shen rolled his eyes, but he did it anyway. He watched as Marc picked up speed and skied *across* the slope, rather than down. He was still playing it safe, Shen realized, being careful of avalanches.

Shen grinned. Then he took a deep breath of crisp mountain air. He'd never admit it, but being out in the wilderness was a real kick. It was the perfect day for it, too. Yesterday's winds had died down, the sun was sparkling, and the blue sky went on forever. He could see why Marc loved it so much.

Marc was in the middle of the slope now. It was steeper there, so he was going pretty fast. He'd nearly made it to the other side, when Shen heard the noise. *Whoomph!* It came from somewhere deep beneath them.

Marc heard it, too. He dropped his ski poles and leaped for the side, plunging his ice-axe deep into the snow.

At first Shen thought it was going to be okay. Deep cracks were spreading across the slope, but Marc was in plain sight, hanging from the ice-axe. Then, as Marc ripped off his skis, the huge slabs of snow started to move. With an almighty roar, the whiteness engulfed him and went crashing to the bottom.

It was all over very quickly. One minute Marc was there, skiing safely across the slope; the next, it was like he'd never existed. Sure, the slope was bumpier than before, but it was white and clean. You'd never know Marc was down there. But Marc was down there, *and it was Shen's fault!* Shen let out a gigantic wail and dropped to his knees.

His first instinct was to go for help. But they were far from anywhere, and if he wasn't quick enough, Marc would… A sharp pain gripped at his chest. *Think!* he told himself. *What had Marc said to do?* Shen took a deep breath and made himself calm down.

The slope had settled now, with no patches of heavy snow above where the avalanche had come from. Shen dug through his pack for his snow shoes and yanked them on. Then he put his **snow probe** together and flicked his two-way radio onto receive.

Shen put on his pack and made his way down to where he'd last seen Marc. He moved quickly, looking and listening carefully as he went. First he found one of Marc's gloves, then he spotted his hat. He followed the fall line down from the hat, zig-zagging and checking the radio constantly.

Shen almost cried in relief when he picked up the signal. He'd found him! He dumped his pack to one side and started probing. It was hard work. Shen repeatedly shoved the probe deep into the snow and dragged it out again. He worked in a grid pattern, concentrating on the area where the signal was strongest. Before long, he was exhausted.

Then the probe hit something solid. Shen snapped his snow shovel together and got digging. The snow had set like concrete, but Shen didn't care. He dug like a maniac. He was going to get Marc out.

But it wasn't Marc that Shen dug out. It was his pack. Shen collapsed onto the snow, and his chest began to heave. It was hopeless. Marc was gone.

Shen felt so upset he could hardly breathe. It didn't matter that he didn't get along with Marc. Losing him was unbearable.

He was still lying there when he noticed something odd on the slope ahead of him. Four tiny bumps were sticking out of the snow. Shen stared at them stupidly. Then he realized. They were fingers! He grabbed his snow shovel and started to dig. First the hand, and then part of the arm was clear; then the head and body.

Marc was very pale, but he was breathing. Shen had never felt so happy. He hauled Marc onto an insulating pad, replaced his lost clothes, and wrapped him in a blanket. Marc waited until Shen was finished. Then he gave him a weak grin.

"My turn to eat snow, eh?" he said.

Graphic Organizer

Action/Reaction Outline

An Action/Reaction Outline lists the main events in a story and shows how they affect the characters. Organizing events like this can help us to understand the consequences and outcomes of events. Look back at the story "Eating Snow." The two main characters start off with certain feelings about each other. Then, during the course of the story, a series of interactions causes these feelings to change.

Interactions

At the beginning

Person 1: Shen

Shen is unhappy because he doesn't want a stepfather.

Person 2: Marc

Marc is trying to make friends with Shen.

Action

Shen falls over.

Reaction

Marc makes a joke of it, and Shen is annoyed.

Action

Shen is in a bad mood. He suggests taking a quicker route home.

Reaction

Marc isn't sure it's safe, but he agrees because he want to keep Shen happy.

Action

There is an avalanche. Marc is buried in the snow.

Action

Shen searches for Marc and rescues him.

At the end

Shen

Shen realizes that he does care about Marc.

Marc

Marc is pleased that the accident has made their relationship stronger, and he can joke about what happened.

Reaction

Shen is scared.

Reaction

Shen is relieved that Marc is okay.

GPS
(Global Positioning System)

Larry Mishima
Coast Guard
200- 210 Bustlee Street
St. John, New Brunswick E2L 6M7

Dear Mr. Mishima,
Next year, some friends and I are going on a boating trip around Cape Breton Island and then to Newfoundland. We're going for two weeks and my friends want to **navigate** using GPS technology.

I haven't used GPS before, and I don't understand how it works. Do all boats have GPS technology installed? We are going to rent a boat from a company in Glace Bay. How will GPS stop us from getting lost or help us if we do get lost?

Yours,
Justine Guerret

Justine Guerret
2 Pembina Road
Regina, Saskatchewan S4F 3E9

Dear Justine,

That sounds like a great trip, and it's good you're getting prepared already. Using GPS (Global Positioning System) is sensible. It's the most accurate way to navigate. With GPS, you can pinpoint your exact location and find out which course you need to take—think of it as an electronic map.

GPS works by using twenty-four satellites that orbit the world about 19 300 km above us. When you request information, your GPS receiver sends a signal up to the nearest satellites. The satellites work out how far away the receiver is and its exact location, then they send a message back to the receiver with this information. GPS works all over the world, twenty-four hours a day, every day of the year, in all kinds of weather. It can help find lost people, ships, cars, and other vehicles in difficult situations like being stuck in blizzards, stormy seas, or high mountain ranges.

To use GPS, you will need a GPS receiver. This looks a bit like a cell phone. Most boats will have one installed, but you should check with the rental company. As well as telling you your current position, a GPS receiver can give you turn-by-turn directions for the course you want to follow and guide you using alert tones. Some receivers will give you information about the tides and water depth and where boat wrecks might be.

Have a great time on your trip!

Kind regards,
Larry Mishima

Lost Memories

Article by Ravi Patel

Usually the things we lose are things we can see, such as car keys or a history assignment. But what happens when you lose something that you can't see, such as a memory?

The Brain's Filing System

Did you talk to anyone at breakfast this morning? Do you remember what you said? How about the name of the person your friend introduced you to last week? And then there's that list of dates for the history test tomorrow! You rely on your memory almost every minute of the day. It's working for you all of your waking hours (and even some of the time you're asleep).

Without your memory, you wouldn't know your name, where you live, or even what you did just a few minutes ago. Your memory is like a giant filing system for information that's managed by your brain. All of the sights, smells, tastes, sounds, and feelings you experience are stored there—often just for a short while, but sometimes for a lifetime. Even when you're asleep, these memories appear in your dreams

Jane
Janine
Janice

1066
The Battle of Hastings

1918
Canadian women given the right to vote

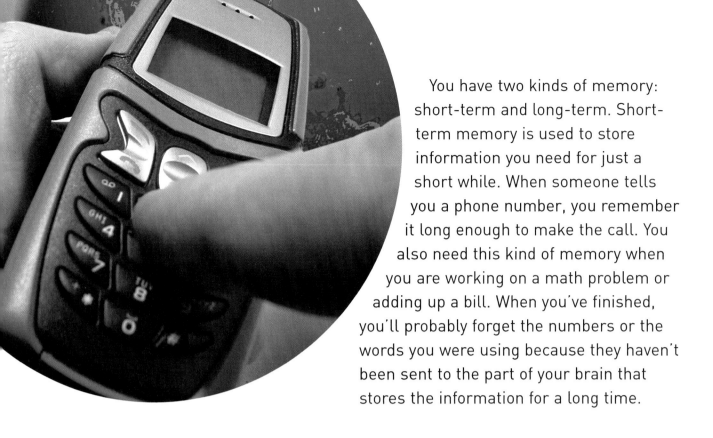

You have two kinds of memory: short-term and long-term. Short-term memory is used to store information you need for just a short while. When someone tells you a phone number, you remember it long enough to make the call. You also need this kind of memory when you are working on a math problem or adding up a bill. When you've finished, you'll probably forget the numbers or the words you were using because they haven't been sent to the part of your brain that stores the information for a long time.

Long-term memory is where important information is filed. It's all the stuff we really want to remember or the skills we need to survive in the world. Each time you jump on a bicycle, you don't have to think about how to ride it. It comes to you automatically from your long-term memory. At other times, you have to search a little to get what you want. For example, when you take a French test, the word you need doesn't always pop into your head immediately. You have to think hard to **retrieve** this kind of information from your long-term memory.

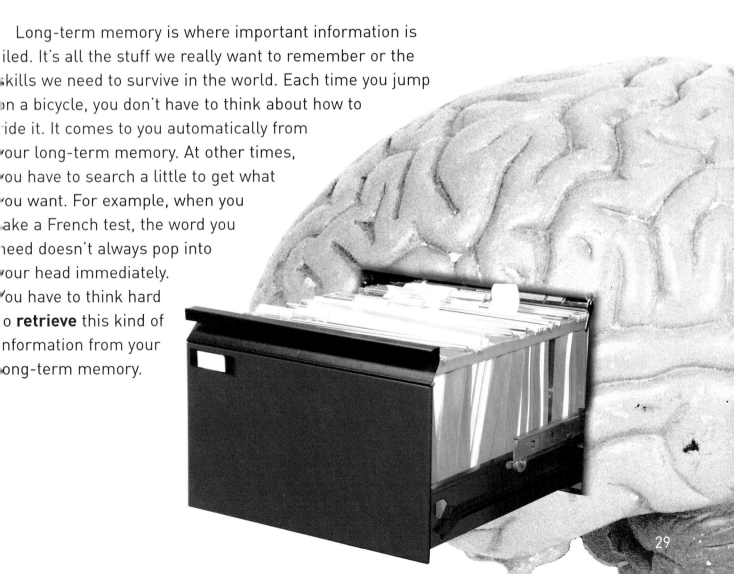

Amnesia

Like every other part of the body, the memory suffers from general wear and tear. As people get older, they find it harder to remember dates and times, or they forget where they've put something. But sometimes an accident, a shocking event, or a disease can cause a condition called amnesia. When you have amnesia, your brain stops storing memories or causes you to lose some of the memories you have stored.

Someone in a bad traffic accident may wake up in a hospital and not be able to remember the accident or being taken to the ER. The shock of the accident has blocked these memories. A person's brain may also block out memories that are too horrible to think about. Soldiers who have been in terrible battles may lose some of their war-time memories.

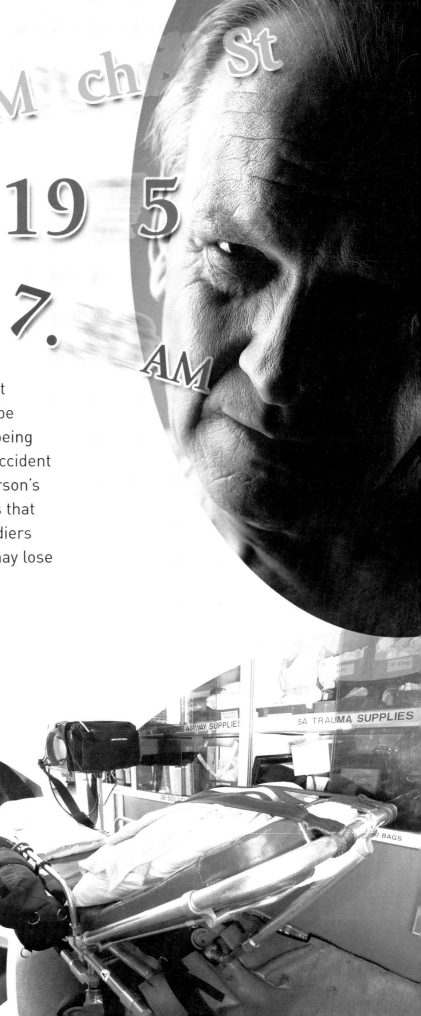

Does Anyone Know ...?

In 1998, an Englishman put an advertisement in the newspaper. The headline was "Does anyone know who on earth I am?" The first thing the man could remember was standing in a railway station. He didn't know how he came to be there.

"As far as I'm concerned, that's where my life began," he said. He didn't know anything about himself—where he lived, what job he did, if he was married or had children. Doctors believed his amnesia had been caused by a shocking event of some kind and that his memory would return after a short time. Happily, friends saw the advertisement and identified the man. To protect his privacy, the rest of his story remains a mystery.

Some scientists compare our memory to a video recorder, catching the information from our senses on tape. However, like a real videotape, the playback sometimes doesn't work the way it should. It gets jammed, or parts of the tape are wiped clean. Information can be lost forever. Thankfully, for most of us, our "memory tape" stays in good condition and we can replay whenever we need to.

Discovery Diary

Explorers and adventurers often keep diaries, describing their experiences and the amazing things they see. Reread "The Lost City of the Incas," the story of the discovery of Machu Picchu by explorer Hiram Bingham, noting his description on page 6. Use information from this article, along with the plan of the city on pages 10 and 11, to write three additional journal entries that focus on the following:

- setting out from the city of Cuzco along the Urubamba River

- impressions on pushing back the jungle foliage for a first view of the city walls

- the different buildings and landmarks in the sectors of the city

Write in a style, or "voice," that you imagine Hiram Bingham would have used in 1911. Include sketches, using images in the article and city plan as references.